level 4

PIANO LESSONS

by JAMES BASTIEN

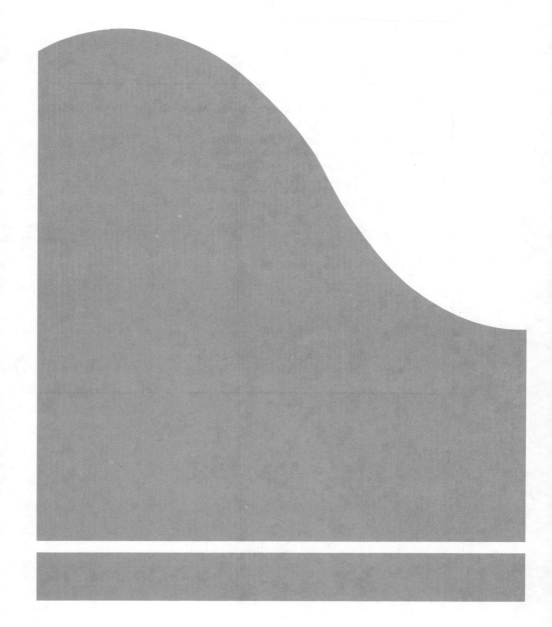

KJOS WEST · Neil A. Kjos Music Co., Publisher · San Diego, California

Preface

PIANO LESSONS leads the student slowly, step by step, through basic keyboard fundamentals. Each level contains original music and carefully selected folk music to provide an enjoyable learning experience. Multi-key reading is introduced gradually in successive levels of the course.

This book is designed to be used in conjunction with the materials listed below.

Suggested Use of Materials with "PIANO LESSONS, Level 4."

After completing **page 5**, the student is ready to begin . . . . **Theory Lessons**-Level 4 (WP10)
After completing **page 6**, the student is ready to begin . . . . **Technic Lessons**-Level 4 (WP15)
After completing **page 13**, the student is ready to begin . . . . **Piano Solos**-Level 4 (WP26)
After completing **page 15**, the student is ready to begin . . . . **Sight Reading**-Level 4 (WP19)
After completing **page 18**, the student is ready to begin . . . . **Piano Literature**-Vol. 1 (GP9)
After completing **page 20**, the student is ready to begin
   these Supplementary Books . . . . **Bastien Favorites**-Level 4 (GP86)
                                                                          Christmas Favorites-Level 4 (WP69)
                                                      Christmas Carols for Multiple Pianos (GP42)
                                                         Country, Western, 'N Folk-Book 1 (GP66)
                                                                                 Duet Favorites-Level 4 (WP63)
                                                                                  The Nutcracker Suite (WP67)
                                                                          Pop Piano Styles-Level 4 (WP54)
                                                                                 Scott Joplin Favorites (GP90)

SHEET MUSIC from **Level Four Solos** may be assigned to the student at the teacher's discretion.

At this point in the **BASTIEN PIANO LIBRARY**, the student has the background to go on to standard piano literature and supplementary materials in Levels 5 and 6 listed on the back cover.

ISBN 0-8497-5004-0

Contents

Prelude in Classic Style

© 1976 Kjos West, San Diego, California
Inter. Copyright Secured   All Rights Reserved   Printed in U.S.A.

You are ready to begin a new book in the **Bastien Piano Library**—"THEORY LESSONS, Level 4."

"Overlapping" Pedal Technic

The DAMPER PEDAL (right pedal) is used to *sustain* and *connect* tones.

The damper pedal is often used in an OVERLAPPING manner.

Practice the following pedal exercises using the "overlapping" pedal.

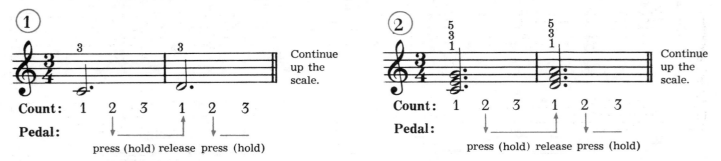

The overlapping pedal is usually shown this way:

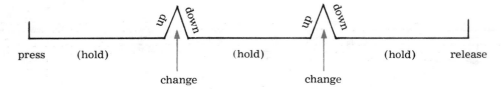

Pedal Studies

You are ready to begin a new book in the **Bastien Piano Library**—"TECHNIC LESSONS, Level 4."

In Church

The Ocean's Roar

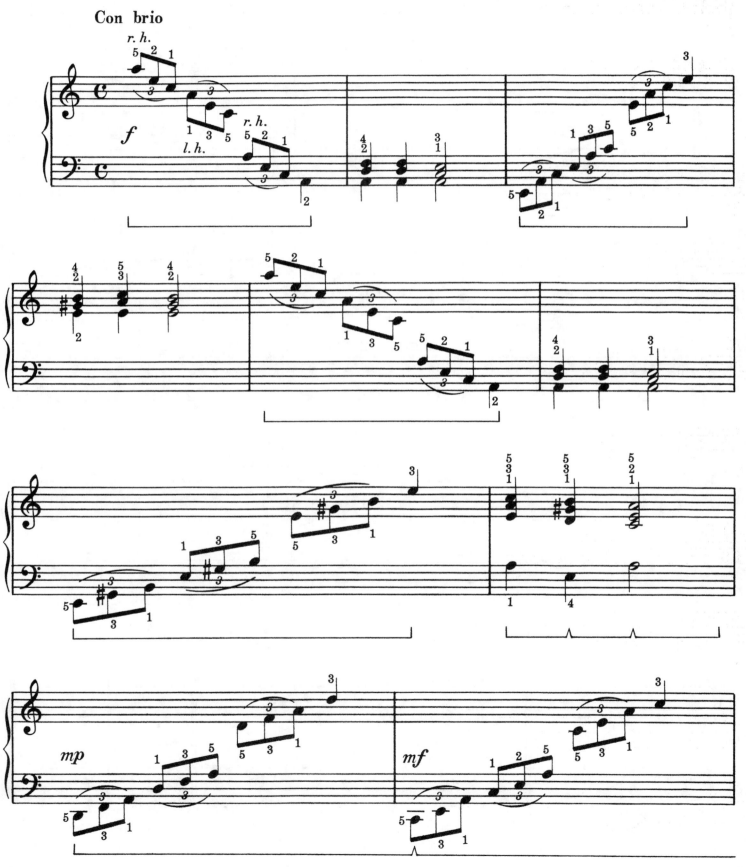

CODA (an added ending)

Intervals of Sevenths

An interval of a seventh is written on the staff as a **line** note to a **line** note, or as a **space** note to a **space** note.

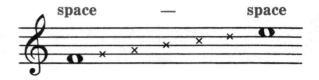

Practice the following interval drills.

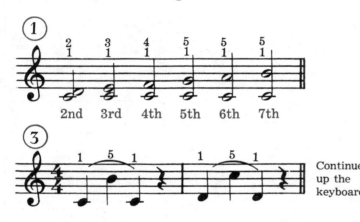

Circle the sevenths used in the two pieces below.

① **Grazioso**

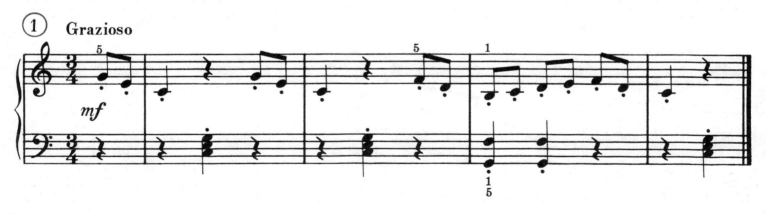

② **Con brio**

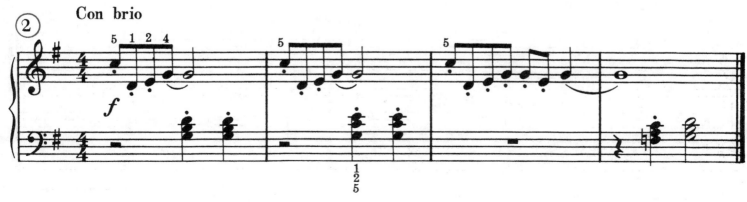

Blues in the Night

Recognizing First Inversion Triads

FIRST INVERSION TRIADS have two notes at the bottom close together (to form an interval of a *third*).

The ROOT is always the top note of the interval of the *fourth*.

Examples:

Find the *first inversion* triads in this group. Circle the root and write the name of each first inversion triad on the blank below.

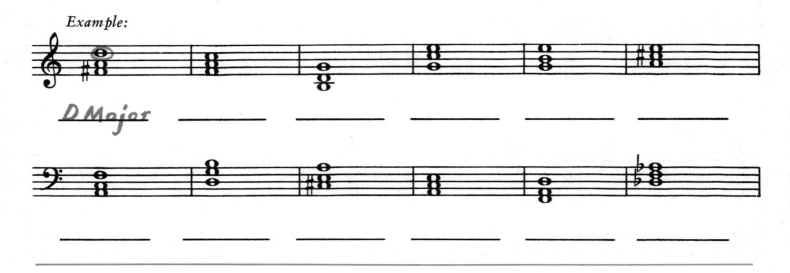

Example:

D Major

Play first inversion triads of the C Major scale. Practice hands separately.

Transpose: G, F

NOTE: When playing in G Major, remember the F♯'s.
When playing in F Major, remember the B♭'s

Chimes

Intervals of Octaves

An interval of an OCTAVE (8th) is written on the staff as a **line** note to a **space** note, or as a **space** note to a **line** note.

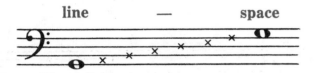

Practice the following interval drills.

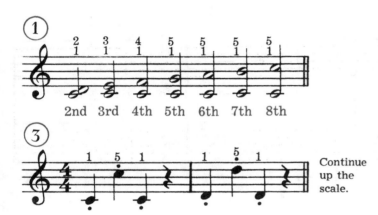

Circle the octaves used in the two pieces below.

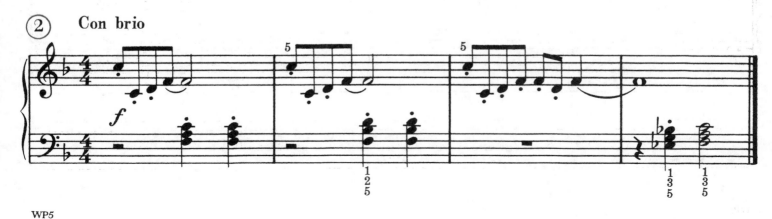

WP5

Grandfather's Clock

You are ready to begin a new book in the **Bastien Piano Library**—"SIGHT READING, Level 4."

Recognizing Second Inversion Triads

SECOND INVERSION TRIADS have two notes at the top close together (to form an interval of a *third*).

The ROOT is always the *top* note of the interval of the *fourth*.

Examples:

Find the *second inversion* triads in this group. Circle the root and write the name of each second inversion triad on the blank below.

Example:

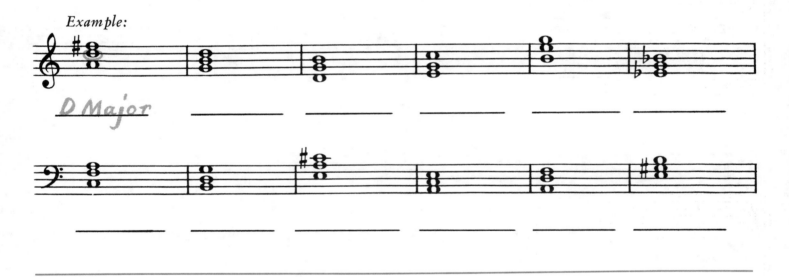

D Major _____ _____ _____ _____ _____

_____ _____ _____ _____ _____ _____

Play second inversion triads of the C Major scale. Practice hands separately.

Transpose: G, F

NOTE: When playing in G Major, remember the F♯'s.
When playing in F Major, remember the B♭'s

Solemn Procession

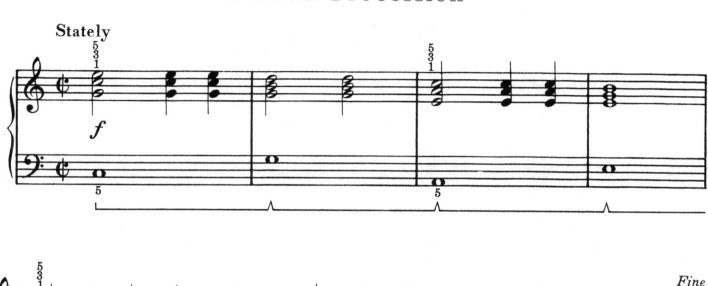

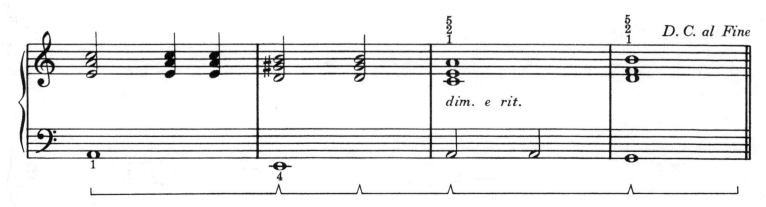

Sixteenth Notes

Four sixteenth notes equal one quarter note.

The four sixteenth notes are often divided.

A single sixteenth note has *two flags*.

Two or more sixteenth notes are connected by a *double beam*.

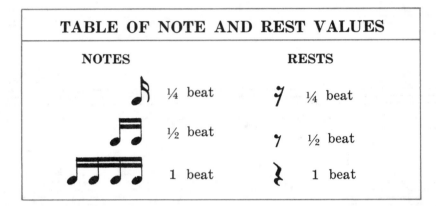

Clap and count the following rhythm.
Use any of the suggested ways for counting sixteenth notes.

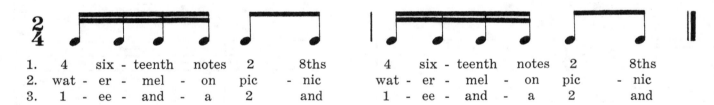

1. 4 six - teenth notes 2 8ths   4 six - teenth notes 2 8ths
2. wat - er - mel - on pic - nic   wat - er - mel - on pic - nic
3. 1 - ee - and - a 2 and   1 - ee - and - a 2 and

Sixteenth Note Etude

Play first with the Right Hand, then with the Left Hand, then with both hands together. Count aloud while you play. Use any of the three ways given above for counting the sixteenth notes.

Transpose to other keys

March of the Marionettes

Clap and count the following rhythm *before* playing **"Country Dance."**

1   and da   2   and   1   and da   2   and

Country Dance

FELIX LE COUPPEY
(1811 - 1887)

Parallel Major and Minor Scales

A minor scale which begins on the *same* keynote as the Major scale is called PARALLEL. The two scales have *different* key signatures.

D MAJOR

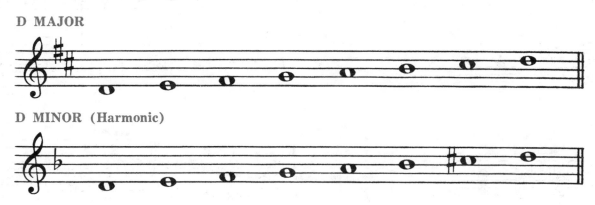

D MINOR (Harmonic)

Practice the following parallel Major and minor scales hands separately.

NOTE: These Major and minor scales have the *same* fingering.

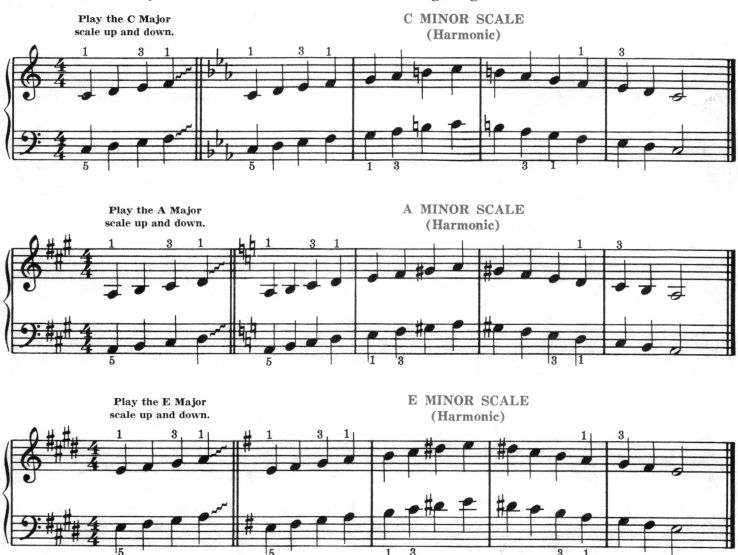

Engine No. 49

Augmented Triads

The word AUGMENT means to make *larger*.

An AUGMENTED TRIAD is formed by *raising* the top note (5th) of a Major triad a half step.

Practice the following chord drill in the Group 1, 2 and 3 keys. Play hands separately at first. Play the Left Hand an octave lower than written.

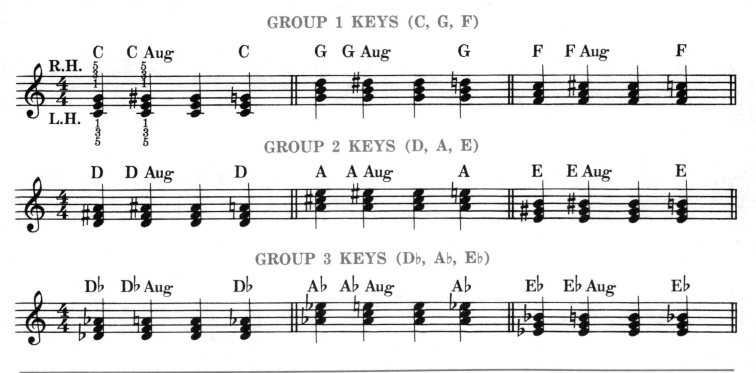

Major-Augmented Triad Etude

Practice the following chord drill hands separately at first. Use the *correct* fingering. Write the name of each chord.

Little Dance

JACOB SCHMITT
(1803 - 1853)

In Italian, "ina" means *little*. The word sonat*ina* is used in the place of the word *sonata* to mean *little sonata*.

The word sonata was first used to mean music "to be played" (music for instruments). Other music was vocal music "to be sung" (music for voices).

A sonatina usually has three movements (parts). The *form* of the first movement is often:
A B   A B   CODA. Notice how this form is used in this sonatina.

Sonatina (First Movement)

OP. 39, NO. 1

FRANK LYNES
(1853 - 1913)

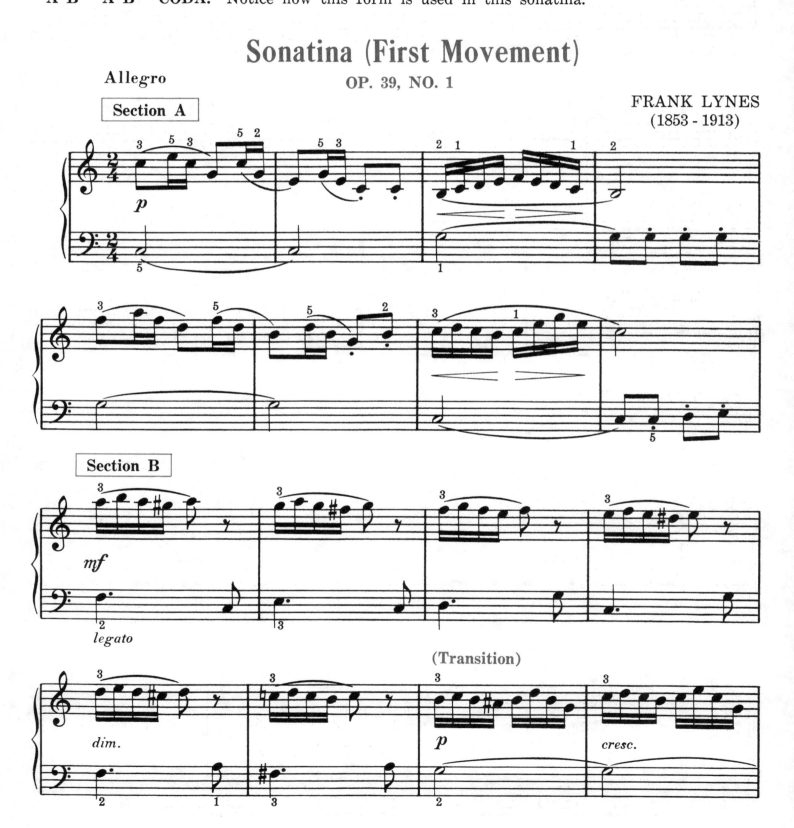

Section A

Section B

legato

CODA

Diminished Triads

The word DIMINISH means to make *smaller*.
A DIMINISHED TRIAD is formed by *lowering* the top note (5th) of a minor triad a half step.

Practice the following chord drill in the Group 1, 2 and 3 keys. Play hands separately at first. Play the Left Hand an octave lower than written.

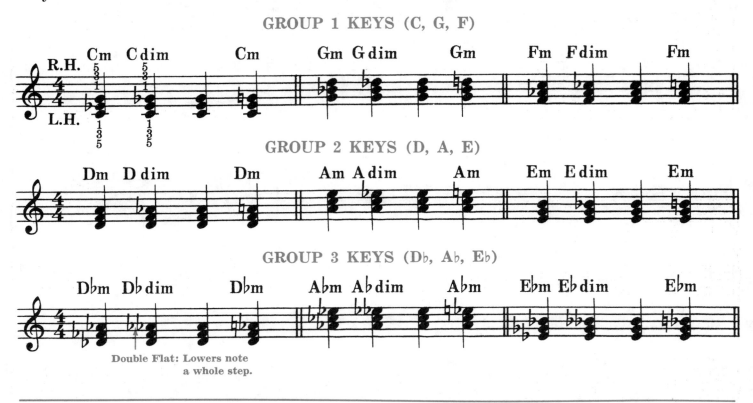

Double Flat: Lowers note a whole step.

Minor-Diminished Triad Etude

Practice the following chord drill hands separately at first. Use the *correct* fingering. Write the name of each chord.

Procession of the Gladiators

Majestic, not fast

Dotted Eighth Note Rhythm

Dotted note rhythm patterns have a *long - short* "feel."

long - short

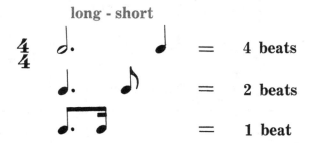

Four sixteenth notes equal *one* quarter note:
A dotted eighth note is equal to *three* sixteenth notes:

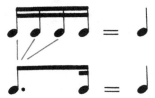

Clap and count the following rhythm. Use any of the suggested ways for counting the dotted eighth note.

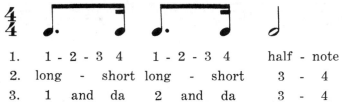

1.	1 - 2 - 3 4 1 - 2 - 3 4	half - note
2.	long - short long - short	3 - 4
3.	1 and da 2 and da	3 - 4

Dotted Eighth Note Etude

Count aloud while you play the following etude. Use any of the three ways given above for counting the dotted eighth note.

Transpose to other keys

The form of this piece is A B C A.

Country Garden

Moderato

ENGLISH FOLK DANCE

Syncopation

SYNCOPATION means to stress or accent weak beats. Often a *long* note is placed on a weak beat. This syncopated rhythm pattern is short - long — short.

Clap and count the following rhythm. Use either of the suggested ways for counting this syncopated rhythm.

Syncopated Rhythm Etudes

Count aloud while you play the following etudes. Use either of the ways given above for counting the syncopated rhythm.

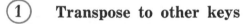

① **Transpose to other keys**

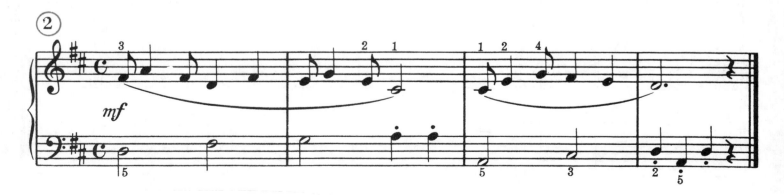

The Bold Bandito

WHOLE-TONE SCALE

A scale made of *whole steps* is called a WHOLE-TONE SCALE. *Six* whole steps played in a row form this scale. The whole-tone scale can begin and end on any of the six notes. There is no "home base" or "tonic" feeling to this scale.

In Outer Space

The Group 4 Keys
UNUSUAL GROUP

> **GROUP 4 KEYS**
> Gb, Bb, B
> **Memorize**

The GROUP 4 KEYS (Gb, Bb, B) have unusual I chords and five finger positions. Each position and chord must be learned separately.

POSITIONS FOR THE GROUP 4 KEYS

> The circled finger numbers outline the I or tonic chords within the five finger positions below. Play the five finger positions and I chords.

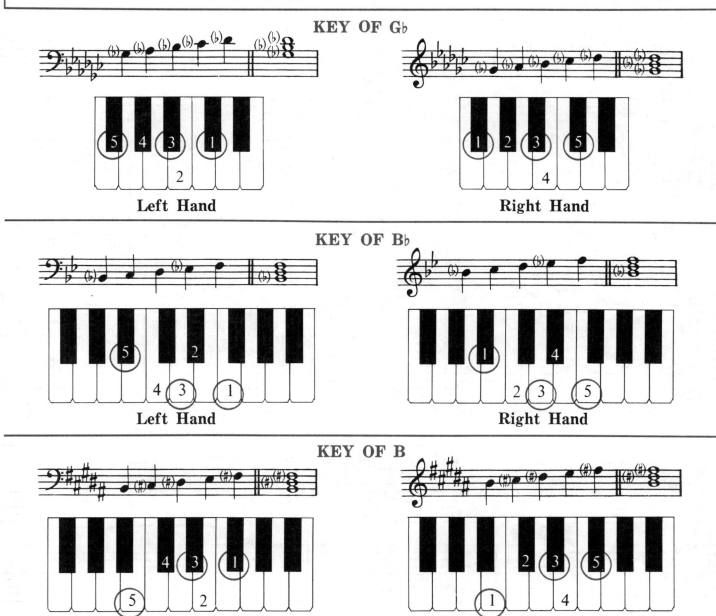

KEY OF Gb
Left Hand   Right Hand

KEY OF Bb
Left Hand   Right Hand

KEY OF B
Left Hand   Right Hand

Reading in G♭ Major

Practice the five finger position and the Primary Chords in G♭ Major *before* playing the three pieces on this page.

*The G♭ Major scale is given on page 46.

Ridin' the Range

Reading in B♭ Major

Practice the five finger position and the Primary Chords in B♭ Major *before* playing the three pieces on this page.

*The B♭ Major scale is given on page 46.

All Alone

Reading in B Major

Practice the five finger position and the Primary Chords in B Major *before* playing the three pieces on this page.

*The B Major scale is given on page 45.

Scottish Bagpipes

Prelude in Romantic Style

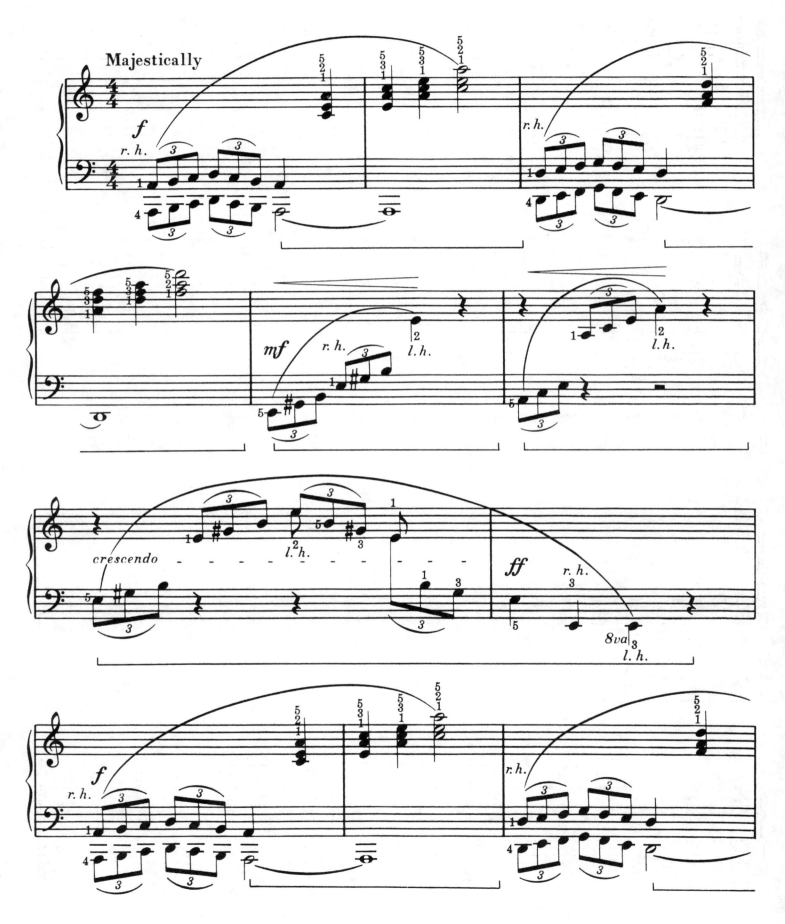

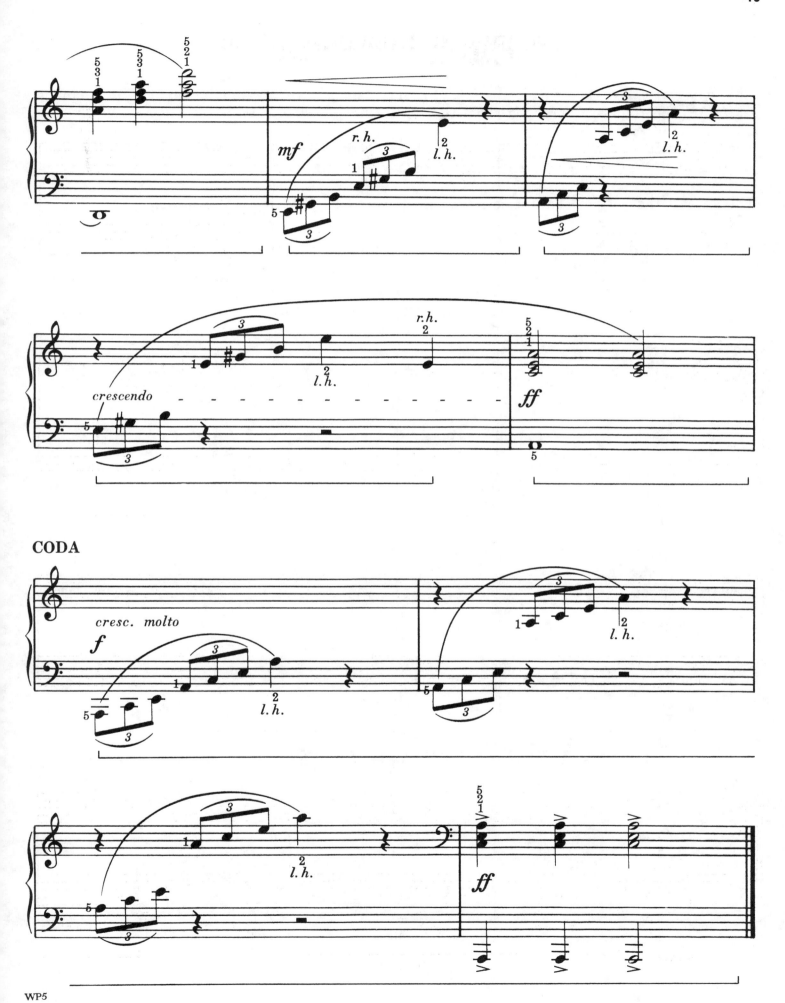

CODA

Circle of Keys

This chart is called the CIRCLE OF KEYS. The sharps are arranged from the top moving *clockwise*. The flats are arranged from the top moving *counterclockwise*.

There are fifteen Major Keys: *seven* sharp keys, *seven* flat keys, *one* with no sharps or flats. Likewise, there are *fifteen* Relative Minor keys.

The keys at the bottom of the circle are called *enharmonic*. These have *two names*.

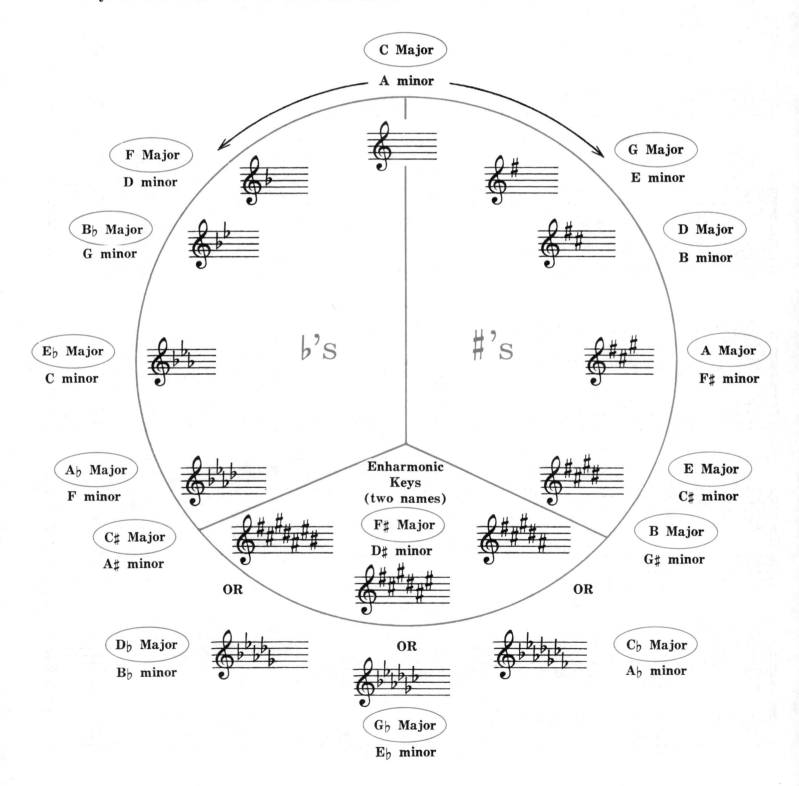

Major Scales and Primary Chords
(SHARP KEYS)

Major Scales and Primary Chords
(FLAT KEYS)